Ogi and the Rugby Match

Ruth Morgan

Illustrations
Michael Price

Gomer

It was the day of the big rugby match.

The Bobinog band were going to sing a song at the start of the match and Nib and Bobin were getting ready to leave.

Ogi was still in the kitchen.

'Come on Ogi,' said Bobin. 'It's time to go. Wow! Is that a rugby ball?'

'No,' chuckled Ogi. 'It's a special cake I've made, covered in chocolate icing. I'm going to give it to the winning team at the end of the match.'

'What a bobintastic idea!' said Bobin.

The Bobinogs started off in their bobivan.
As they were driving along, they saw a bus.

'Look!' said Nib. 'That's Brenda's bus. She's driving all our friends to the stadium.'

'Please hold the cake steady!' said Ogi. 'We're nearly there.'

The stadium was full of cheering fans.

'Hi! We're the Bobinogs!' Nib said into the microphone. 'We're going to sing you a song before the teams come on!'

'Who's going to be the fastest team?
Abernog or Bobipandy?
Who's going to kick and throw and catch?
Who's going to win the rugby match?'

The teams ran on and the crowd went wild.
Then the match began.

'Come on, Abernog!' shouted Nib and Bobin. 'Run with the ball! Score a try!'

'I'd love to give my cake to the Abernog team,' Ogi said to himself. 'I hope they win.'

Whoops! One of the Bobipandy players kicked the ball so hard, it flew right out of the stadium.

'Oh no!' said Bobin. 'What's going to happen now?'

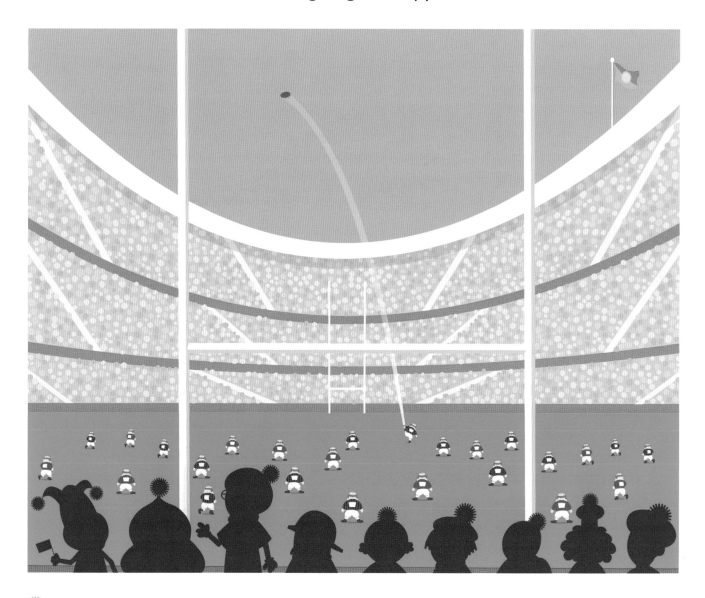

'Diddly no! Don't panic,' shouted Fireman Prout. 'Ogi's brought a spare ball. Come on Abernog!'

And Fireman Prout threw Ogi's cake onto the pitch!

'Help! My cake!' shouted Ogi. He ran onto the pitch to rescue the cake but the teams had already started playing with it.

'This ball is very slippery and muddy,' said one of the Abernog players.

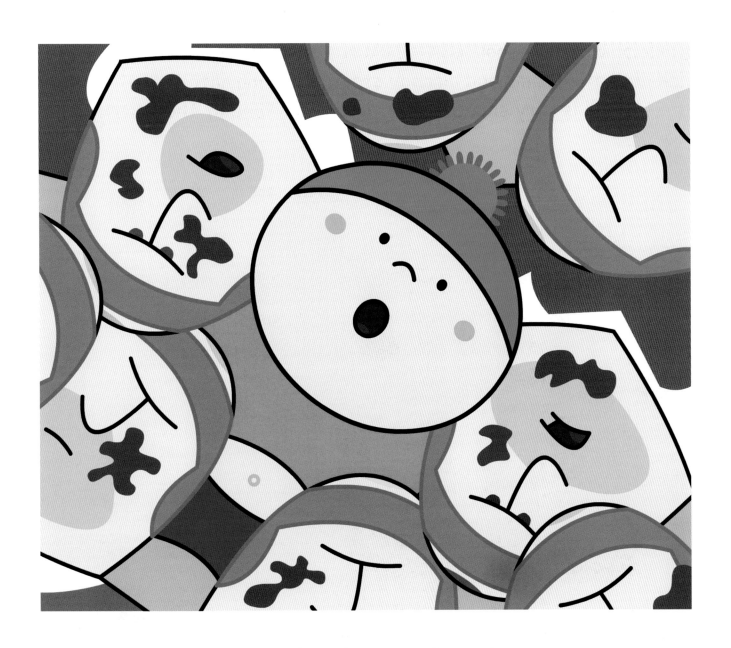

'That's not mud. That's chocolate icing!' cried Ogi.
But it was so noisy in the scrum, nobody could hear him.

Ogi grabbed the cake and started running up the pitch, away from the Bobipandy players.

'Come on, Ogi!' everyone shouted. 'You're going to score a try! Ogi, Ogi, Ogi! Oi, Oi, Oi!'

One of the Bobipandy players tackled Ogi and he fell over the line. He had scored the winning try for Abernog! The only trouble was, his cake was all squished on the floor.

'We've won, thanks to Ogi!' shouted the Abernog team.

The crowd clapped and cheered for Ogi.

'I'm sorry! Diddly-no! I diddly-didn't realise that ball was a cake,' said Fireman Prout.

'Never mind,' said Mam-gu Bobiknot. 'I brought a cake today, too. A trophy cake for the winning team: Abernog!'

And Ogi got the biggest slice, of course!